We Ski

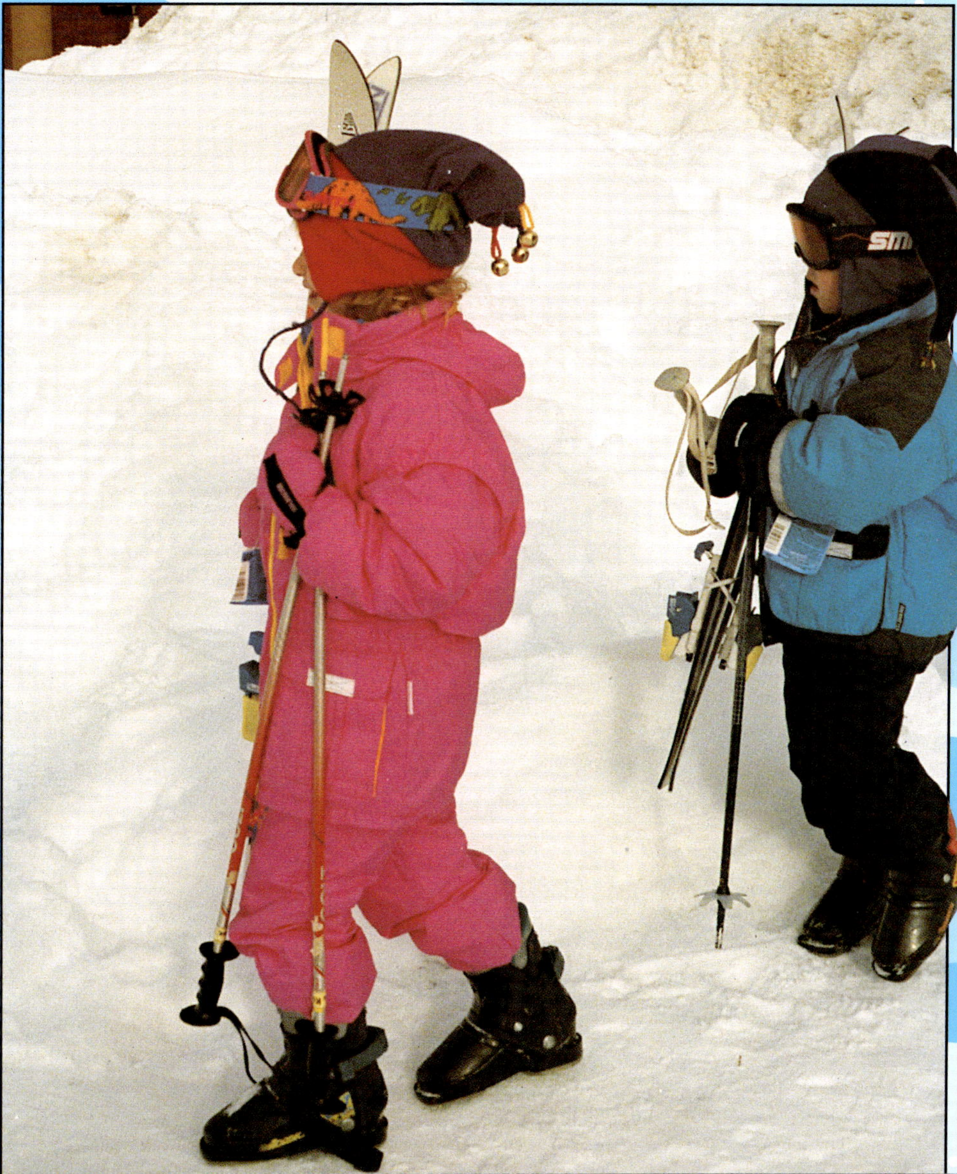

We put on
our jackets.

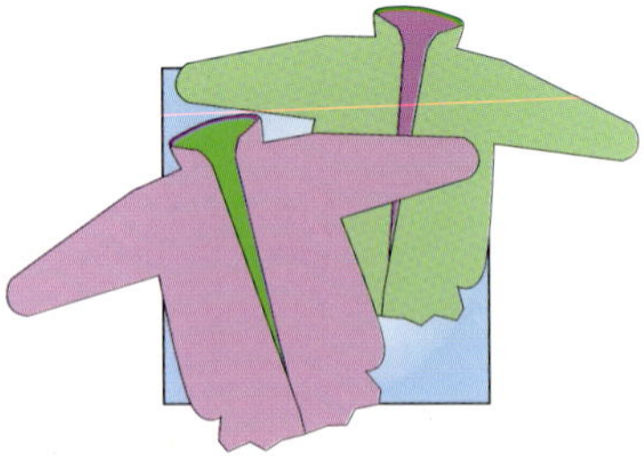

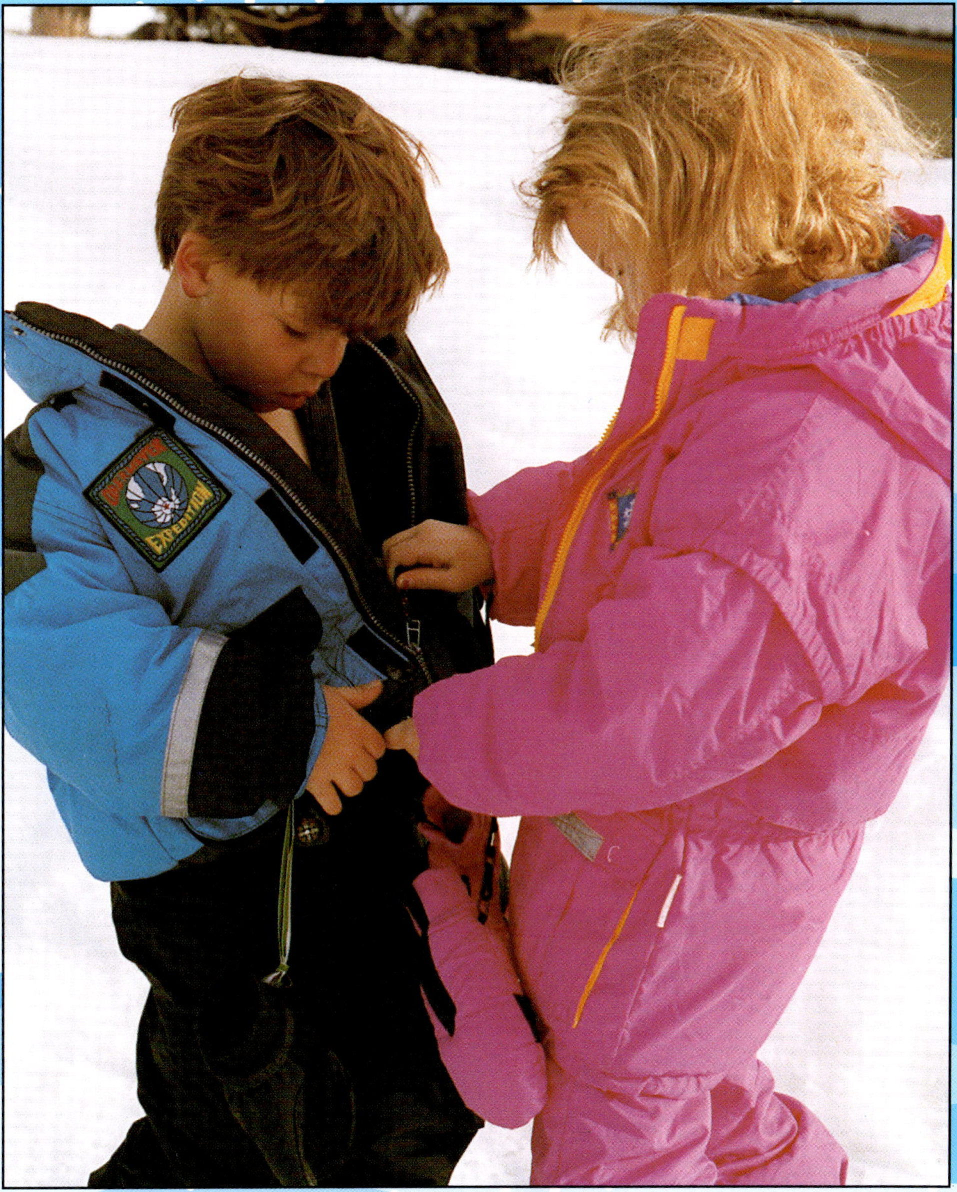
EXPEDITION

We put on
our hats.

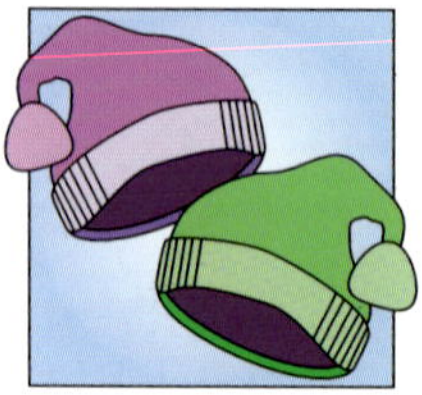

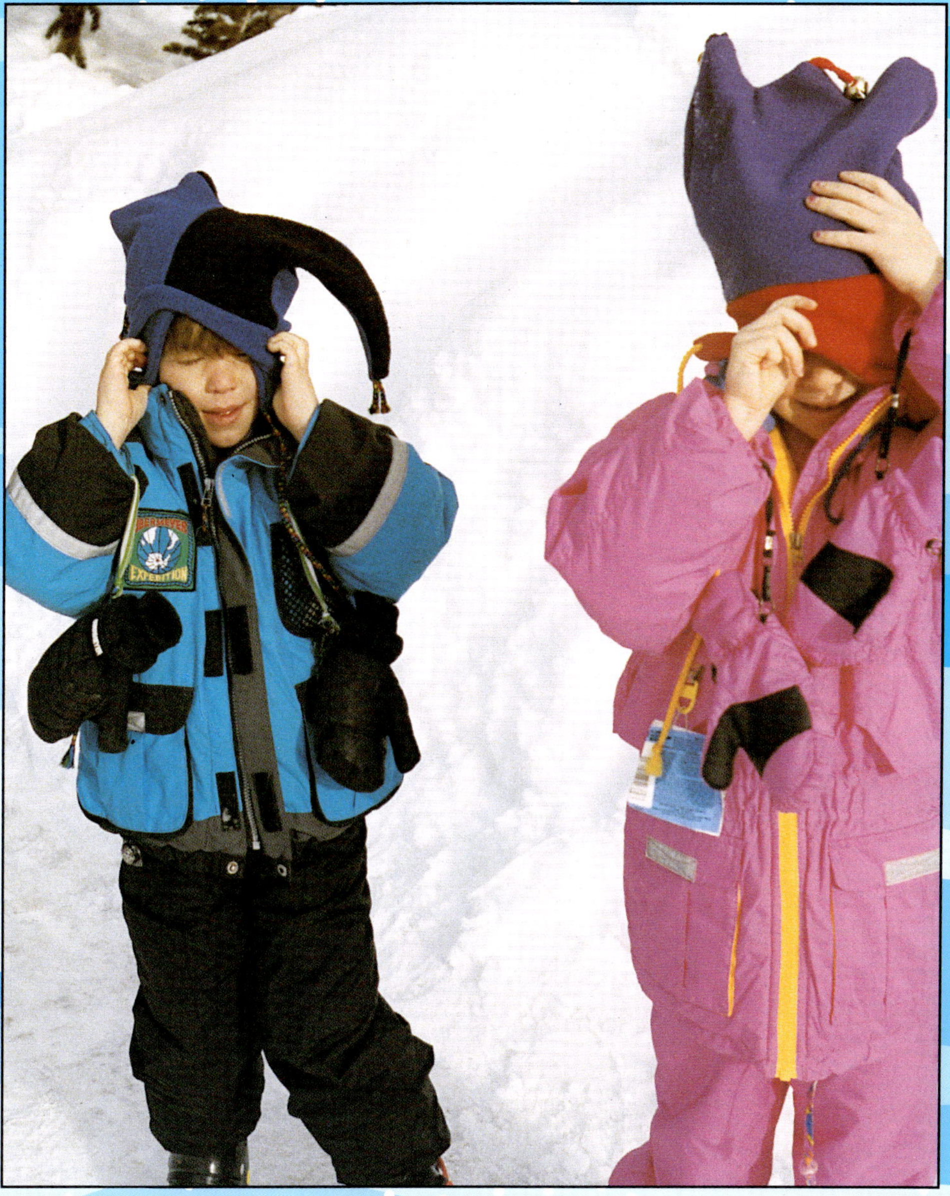

We put on our goggles.

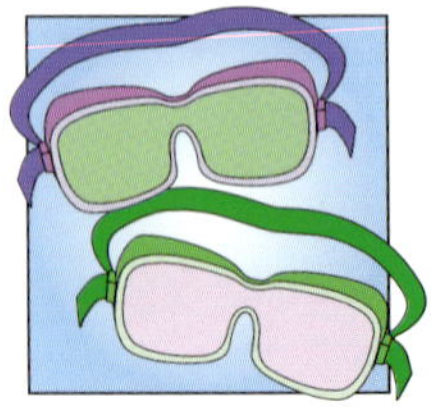

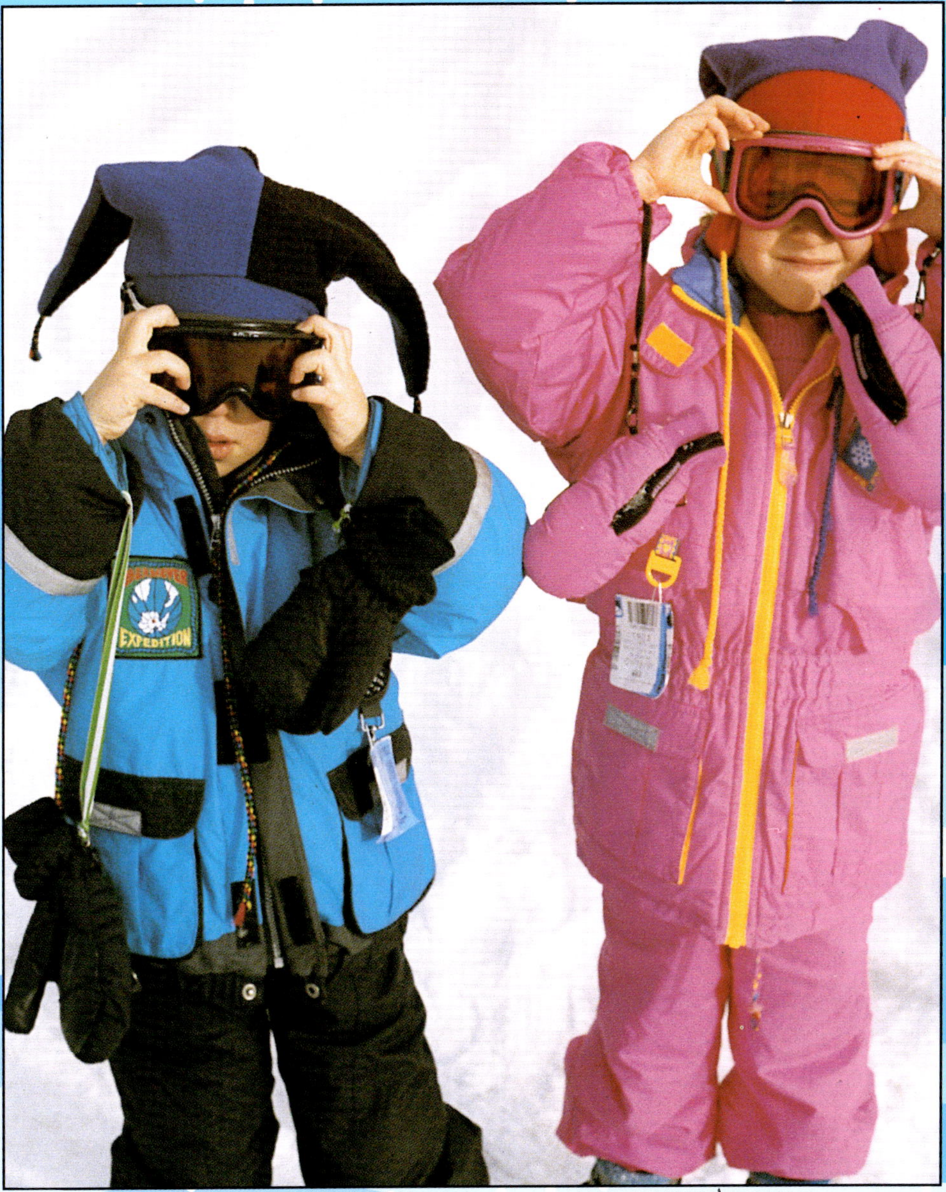
EXPEDITION

We put on
our boots.

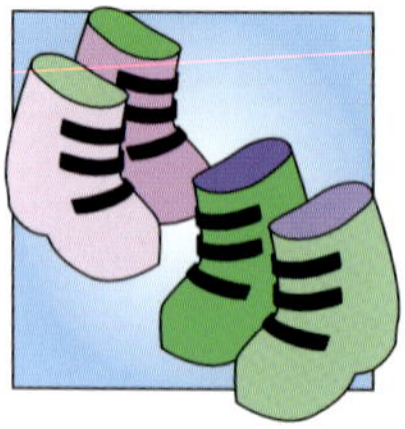

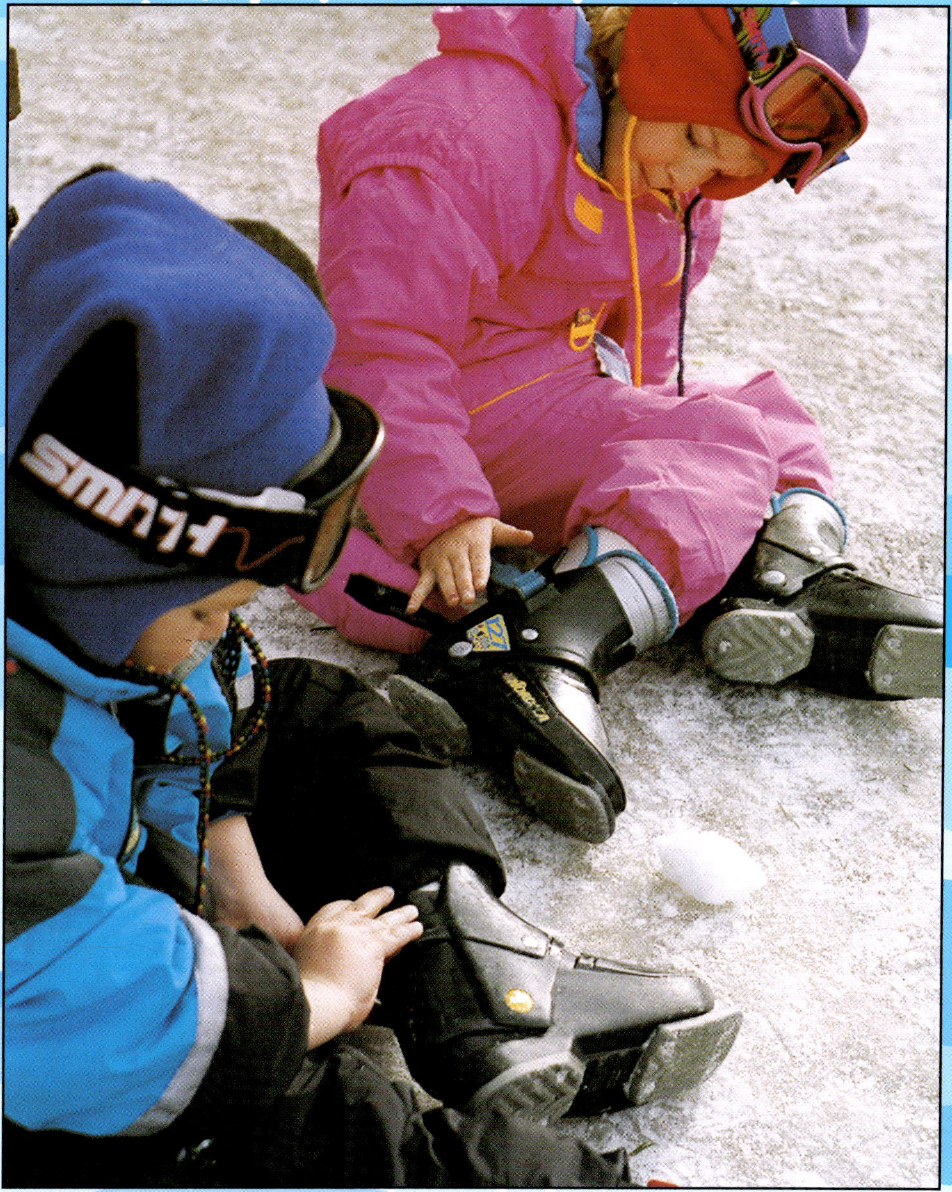

We put on
our mittens.

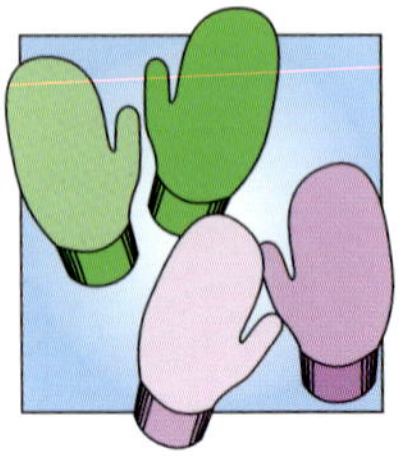

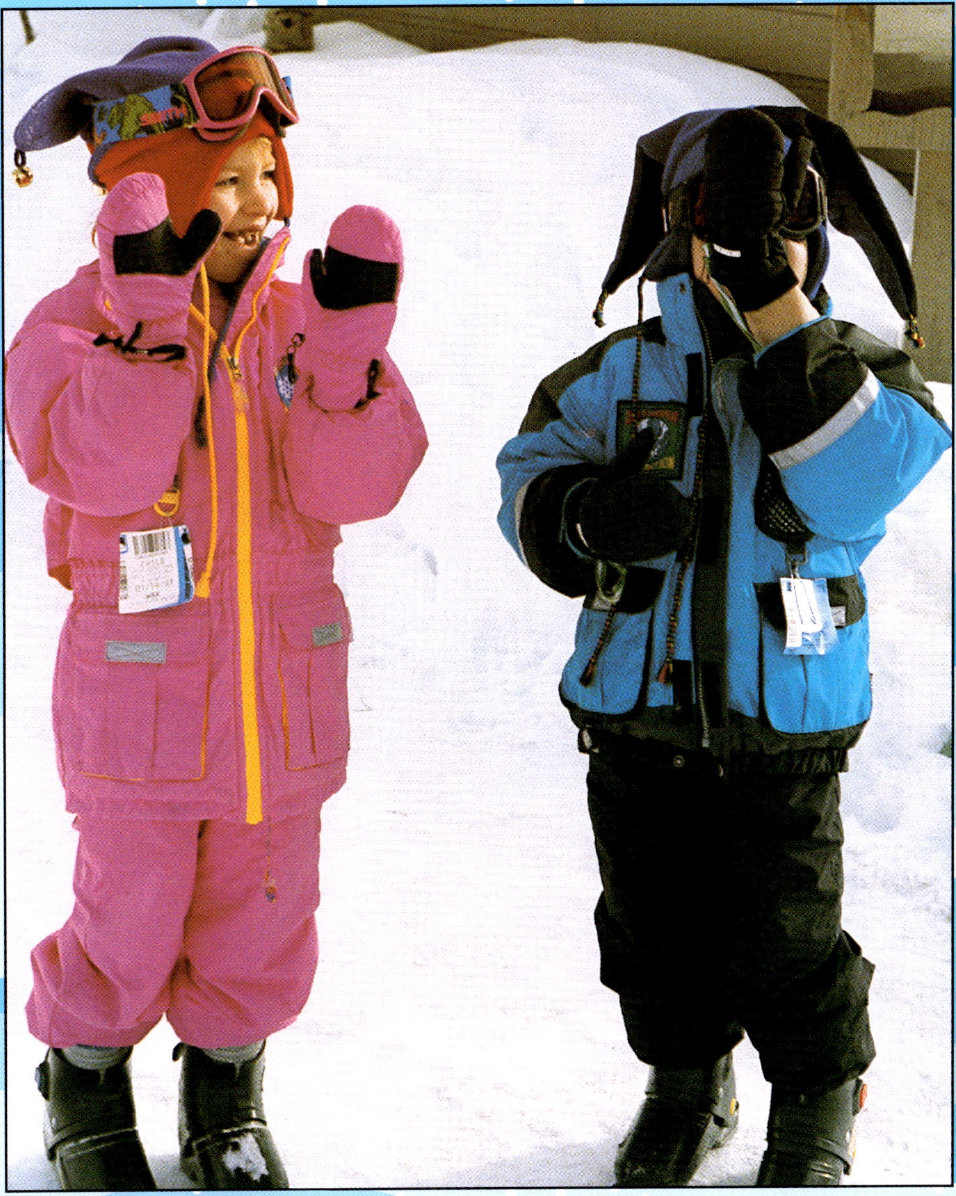

We go
up, up, up.

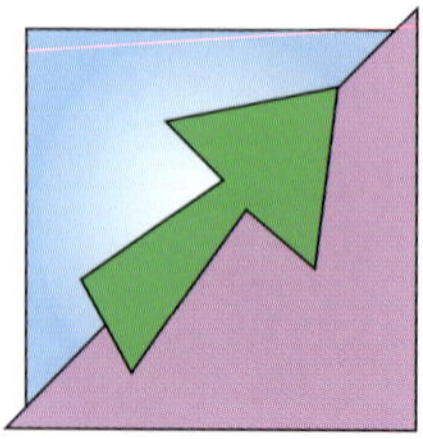

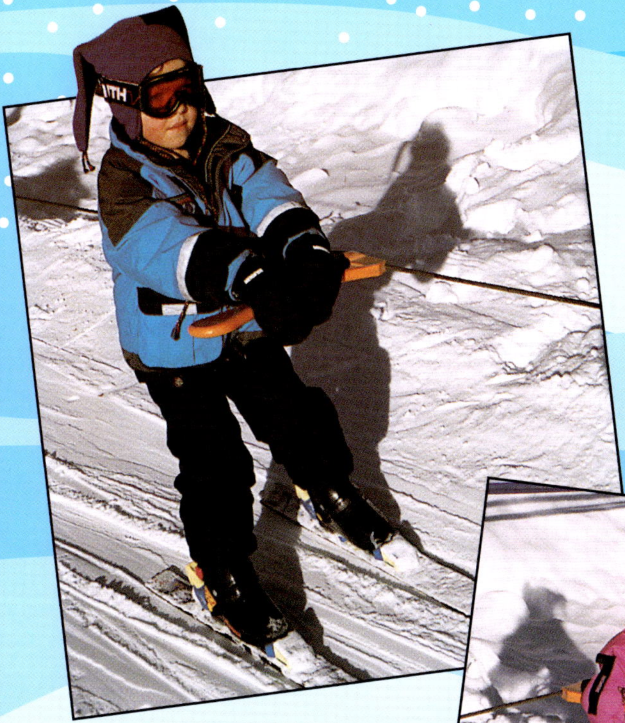

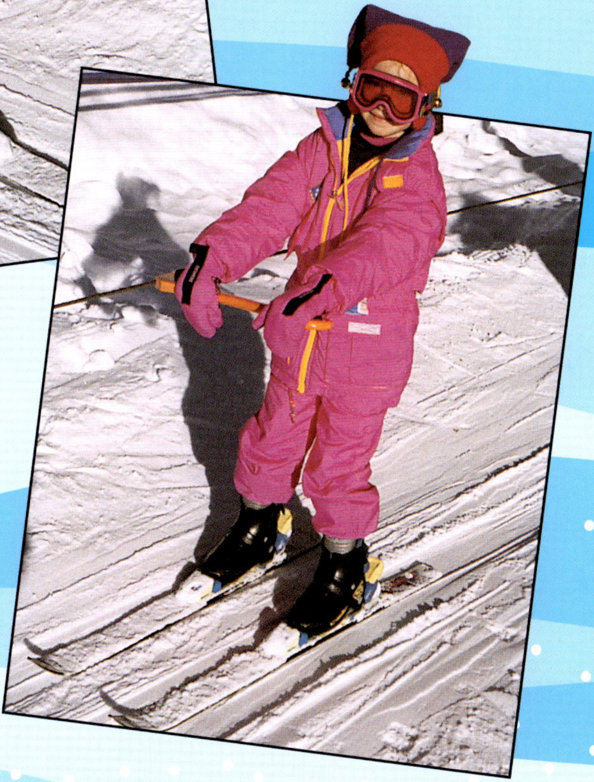

We ski
down, down, down!

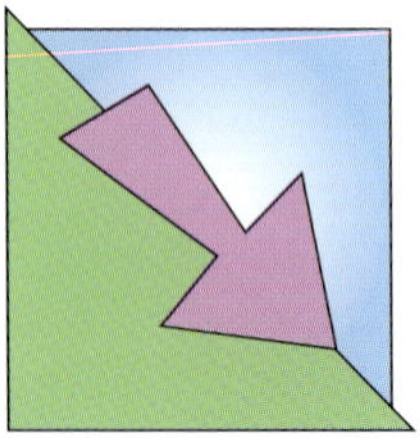

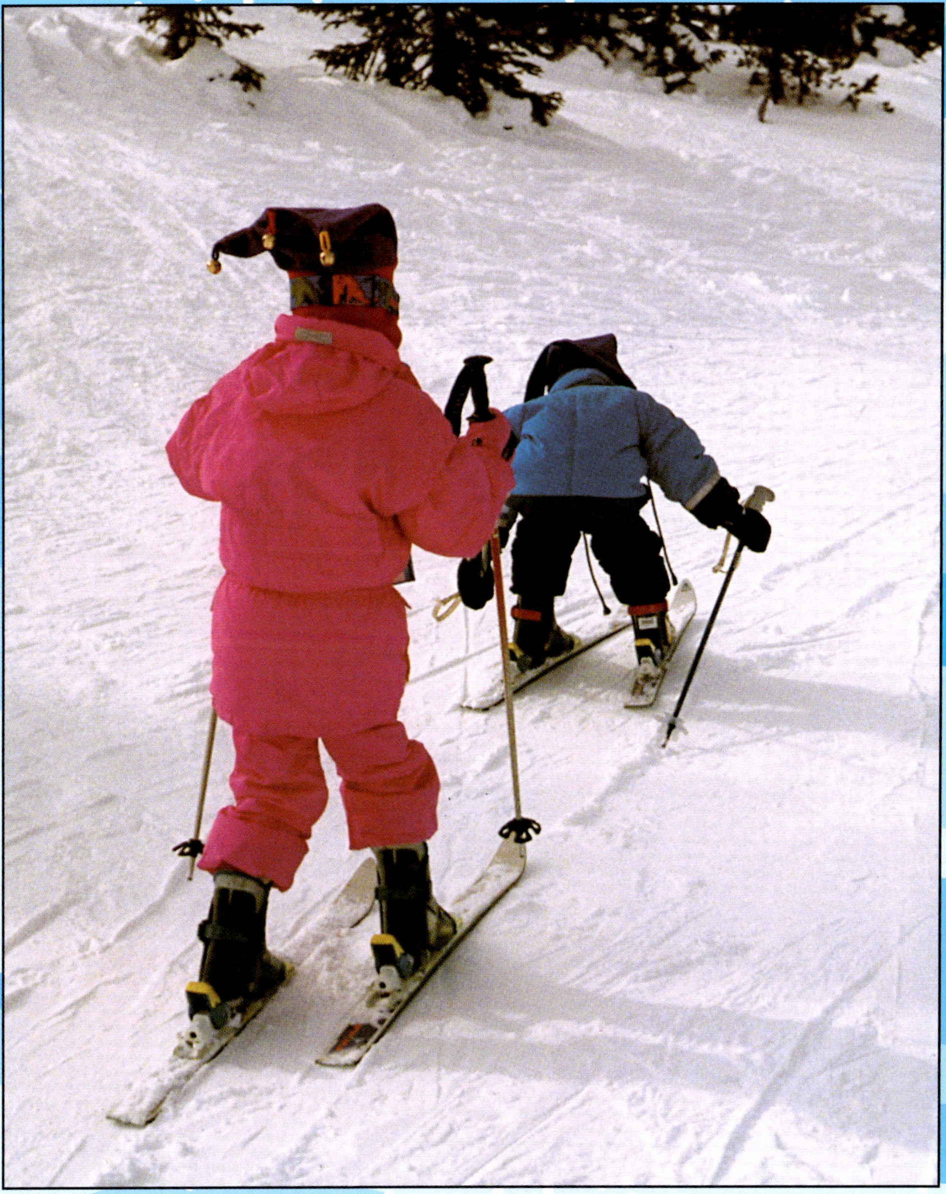

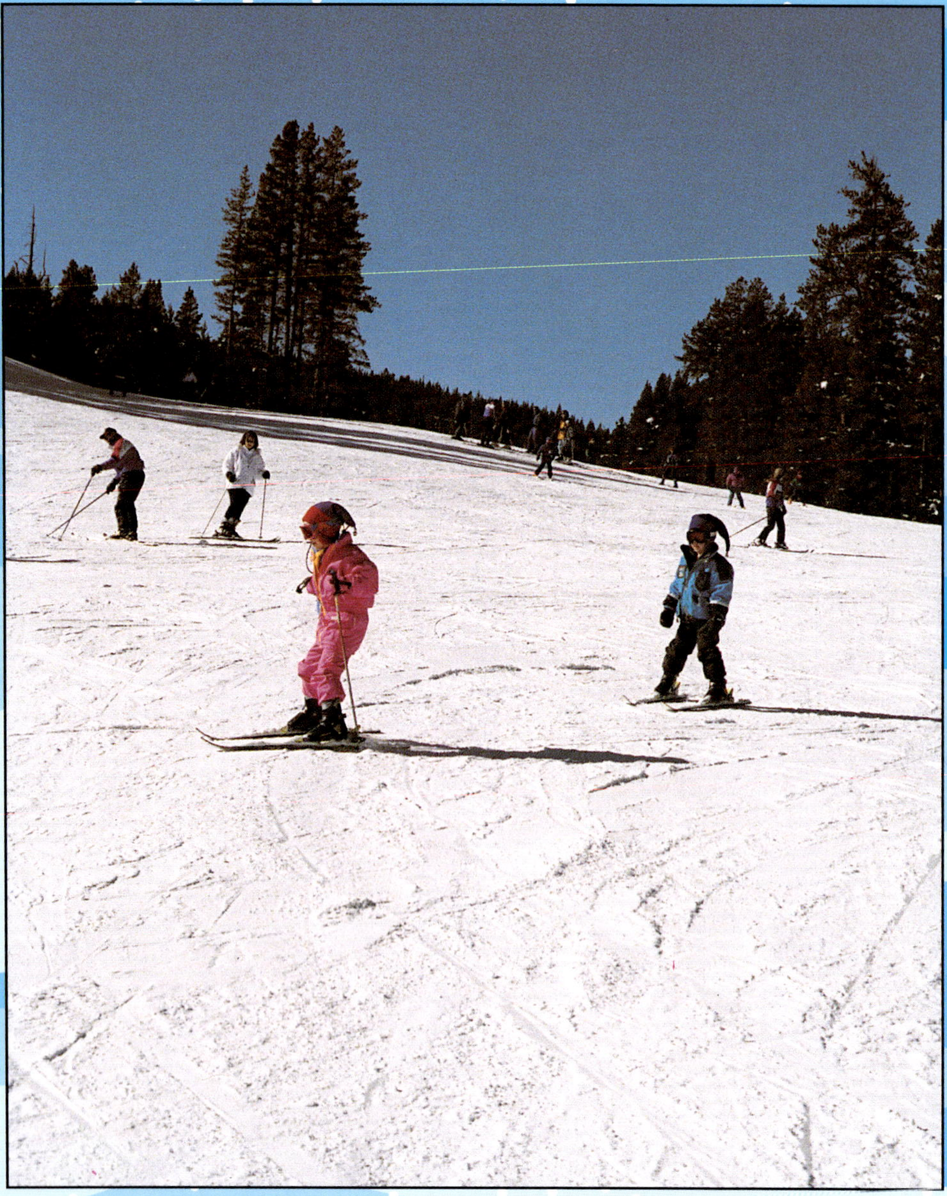